# A LANGUAGE PREPRIMER

**Marilyn M. Toomey**

illustrated by
**Kevin M. Newman**

CIRCUIT PUBLICATIONS

Marblehead, MA

Copyright ©1996
by Circuit Publications
PO Box 1201
Marblehead, Mass. 01945
All rights reserved.

01 00 99 98 97 TS 6 5 4 3 2

ISBN:  0-923573-24-0

Printed in the United States of America on recycled paper.

*A Language Preprimer*

# TABLE OF CONTENTS

*A Language Preprimer*

# FOREWARD
## by
### Robert Chubrich, Ph.D.

Stephen Pinker, in his book, *The Language Instinct*, says that in modern life the race is not to the swift but to the verbal. At the risk of battering an already open door, this book, *A Language Preprimer* is offered as a tool to help you complement and enrich the vocabularies that children bring to school. It can also be used as another avenue for home-school connections.

Stephen Pinker writes that language is so important that it is hard to imagine life without it. Phyllis Martin says that words can change the direction of your life. With words you relate to people, influence them, persuade them and communicate your feelings to them. Even though you have a comparably good vocabulary, your mind will never develop its full potential, for words are your tools for thinking - and words can make you feel great. This is a book designed to help you share words with children.

In 1990 the president and the governors of fifty states established six national goals. The first of these states that by the year 2000 all children in America will start school ready to learn. It is possible to hear echoes in this goal from the goals of the 1960's when programs such as Head Start were created to help children move from poverty to self-sufficiency. Creating new programs to educate children at risk was seen as a means of lessening academic failure, welfare dependency and delinquent behavior.

Unfortunately, the goals of the 60's and the 90's stand in stark contrast to the reality that today many American children continue to come to school without the knowledge to fully benefit from school. This is not to say that setting ambitious national goals is a bad idea. If establishing such goals could galvanize the action of people to even partially meet them there would be great dividends in the quality of life of children and concomitant benefits for society. If somehow children could be immunized against school failure and the associated social consequences we would all be winners.

Something which seems irrefutable is that in order to thrive in school children must have adequate language skills; they must have words. Having a large vocabulary is associated with school success. According to Richard Anderson and William Nagy in the American Educator (Winter, 1992), there are about 88,500 distinct words in printed English. The average high school senior knows about 40,000 words. The average child in elementary school and high school learns 2,000 to 3,000 new words each year. Moreover, there is an average of four meanings per word in school dictionaries.

I had an experience as a graduate student many years ago that still evokes bad memories. I enrolled in a computer class that was advertised as a beginning class. The class actually turned out to be quite advanced, made up of students who had considerable background in the subject. The feeling of being "lost" was a very unpleasant experience for me, and I believe still colors my feelings about computers. Experiences such as my own should sensitize us to the feelings of children who come to school not ready to learn.

School can be a wonderful and exciting place where children thrive and realize their full potential. School can also be a punishing experience for children who are unprepared. Different children will bring different experiences to school and the many new words waiting there to be learned. Some children will have had rich and varied experiences and will have much knowledge to map onto words that you introduce. This is sometimes called "bottom up" learning. Some children will have heard these words and even used them. These children will seem like "quick studies" compared to those children encountering these words for the first time.

When children come to you with a rich set of experiences to connect with the words you present, this is a case of "the rich get richer." Learning certain words that you present might pose new challenges for some children. At the same time these same words for other children can act as catalysts to exercise knowledge that they already have, knowledge and language that they can readily express as you engage them in conversation.

When you present a word that is new for a child this is the case of "top down" learning. Ideally, someone in the child's environment (home and school) can help the child notice new instances of referents of the word. I recall working with a young boy with Down's Syndrome. I introduced the word "stuck" when he was looking at a bulldozer that was stuck in a hole. He repeated the word several times but did not appear to know what it had to do with the bulldozer. During the latter part of that day his mother pointed out several other instances of objects being "stuck." She reported that the child did fine in understanding her use of the word until she used it to refer to being "stuck" in traffic.

New words can serve to help us notice things in the world that have not previously gained our attention. A common experience people report is when buying a particular kind of car they begin noticing this same kind of car in traffic to a much greater extent. Likewise, a child will notice words that have been presented formally in school as these words occur around incidentally.

Something which cannot be stressed too strongly is the fact that when you help a child learn a new word or strengthen her knowledge of a word you are really strengthening her foundation for literacy. Language is unitary; it is connected. The child will understand and say a word and later be able to read and write it. We come across words in our reading that we eventually incorporate into our expressive vocabularies.

At the same time it is important to remember that there are many important differences between talking and writing. Written text is not speech written down. Many children are fortunate to have been read to. This will make learning to read easier for them. They have been exposed to the features of written narrative before they begin formal literacy instruction. In addition many children have had their oral narratives shaped by their listeners. This will facilitate learning to write.

When you attempt to introduce new vocabulary to children this requires a certain degree of metalinguistic awareness on the part of the child. You will be using language to talk about language. A new word, rather than being a transparent vehicle of communication, will be the object of conscious attention. Children need metalinguistic awareness to acquire literacy skills.

In the second paragraph of this foreword I refer to Stephen Pinker's comment that language is so important that it is hard to imagine life without it. It might be easier than he thinks. Observing children with poor language skills as they experience many difficulties in school gives us some insight into life without language. Language is the linchpin of a child's life in school, the world of learning and literacy. As a young learner enters this domain simple, direct materials addressing word learning will help build a strong foundation for future school success. *A Language Preprimer* is indeed such a tool.

# INTRODUCTION

*A Language Preprimer* was prepared to give teachers or language specialists a means of introducing young children to many of the words included in early reading materials. The importance of a child's vocabulary as part of her readiness for emergent literacy has been presented remarkably well in Dr. Chubrich's foreword. As children enter school they will soon meet the challenge of understanding and expressing information in print. The language that has been used to talk and to understand speech must be converted into a new medium. In some ways it's like learning another language!

This book is designed to present a number of words used in many early reading materials, in stories or occurring along with simple paper-and-pencil activities. These words are presented in a way that the words themselves are focal points. The pages of this book might serve to support lessons presenting vocabulary or concept development.

The first section, pages 2-23, presents familiar people, animals and objects grouped into recognizable categories. Each of these groups includes pictures, a list of related terms and some statements or questions intended to stimulate a child's discussion of his own experiences with these people or things. Children should attend to the pictures and to your discussions rather than to the words printed on these pages. Presentation of these concepts and vocabulary should be as though an adult is reading a book to the child.

The next three sections, pages 24-87, target terms denoting relational concepts, miscellaneous frequently-occurring function words and contrasting pairs of descriptive terms. Here, children focus on one or two words at a time, listening to each word and recognizing it in simple, familiar contexts supported by illustrations. For chidden whose speech and language development might have been delayed such attention to certain individual words is essential. Often children omit unstressed words in utterances, saying only the words which carry most of the meaning. Also, for some children who speak other languages, small relational concept terms (such as *of, on, in*) might not have a one-to-one translation into English. Rather, meanings conveyed by such words in English might be incorporated into other words of their language. Focusing on often-unstressed words will help children recognize them later in reading and phonics lessons. For each word or pair of words there is one or more pictures and questions or statements encouraging students to express target words talking about their own experiences or about things that should be very familiar to them.

The last two sections, pages 88-121, introduce terms and ideas that the young learner will meet in basic readiness activities. In this section the type size has been increased. This is to simulate instructions printed on readiness worksheets. Young learners should be introduced to the idea that words occurring on a page are associated with the activity on that page. The user is encouraged to discuss the target concepts and associated terms, though not expecting the child to read the print. Activities focusing on words such as *same/different*, *opposite*, *go together*, and *rhyme* are intended to help children become familiar with the concepts, the words and the notion that activities are associated with printed instructions.

This book should help you organize presentations and instruction for students working to improve vocabulary and concept development. These early efforts to build the foundations of literacy in your young students are most important in helping them get ready to read. I hope *our* presentations here in this book help you with yours!

*Marilyn*

# Family and Friends

This is Nancy. Nancy is five years old.

This is Mike. He is seven years old.

This is Eric, Mike and Nancy's baby brother.

This is Mike, Nancy and Eric's father. His name is Andy.

This is Mike, Nancy and Eric's mother. Her name is Alice.

Here is Mike, Nancy and Eric's grandmother.

Here is their grandfather.

Here is their Uncle Marcus.

Here is Mike, Nancy and Eric's Aunt Sally.

Aunt Sally and Uncle Marcus have a son. His name is Rodney. Rodney is Mike, Nancy and Eric's cousin.

Do you have brothers or sisters?
Do you have aunts, uncles and cousins?
Talk about your grandparents.
Talk about your friends.

*A Language Preprimer*

# Family and Friends

Alice, Andy and their children, Mike, Nancy and Eric live next door to Carol and Steve. They are neighbors.

Carol and Steve have a son, Kenneth, a daughter, Susan and a baby, Katie. Kenneth and Susan are Mike and Nancy's friends.

Here are Kenneth and Susan's grandparents.

The grown-ups are friends too.

Who are some of your neighbors?
Name some women, men, girls and boys who you know.

## Words to Help You Talk about People

| | | | |
|---|---|---|---|
| adult | father | grown-up | parents |
| aunt | friend | husband | teenager |
| baby | girl | infant | uncle |
| boy | grandfather | man | wife |
| child | grandmother | mother | woman |
| cousin | grandparents | neighbor | |

# A House, a Place to Live

Talk about the place where you live.

What are some places and special things on the street where you live?

What is special about your neighborhood?

What are some of the things outside your house, in your yard?

Talk about places where you like to play that are near your house.

Sometimes you must be careful when you play outside. What are some things Mom and Dad talk about when they tell you to be careful?

# A House, a Place to Live

Here are some things you might see near a house.

**Words to Help You Talk about Things Near Your House**

| | | |
|---|---|---|
| apartment | garden | sandbox |
| balcony | grass | shrubs |
| bushes | lawn | sidewalk |
| carport | lobby | street |
| condo | mailbox | swing |
| deck | nest | tree house |
| driveway | patio | trees |
| fence | porch | window |
| garage | roof | yard |

# Inside the House

Talk about the rooms in your house.

Talk about your room and some of your special things.

What are the rooms in your home where your family prepares and eats breakfast, lunch, dinner and snacks?

Talk about the room where your family spends time together relaxing and doing things together.

What are some places in your home where people work hard?

How do you decorate your house for holidays or parties?

# Inside the House

### Kitchen

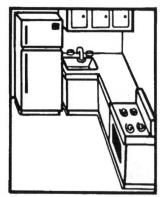

| | |
|---|---|
| blender | knife |
| bowls | microwave |
| cabinet | mixer |
| coffee maker | oven |
| cold water | pans |
| counter | pantry |
| cups | plates |
| drain | pots |
| faucet | refrigerator |
| food | sink |
| fork | spoon |
| freezer | stove |
| glasses | toaster |
| hot water | |

### Dining Room

buffet
candles
centerpiece
chairs
china cabinet
cups
dishes
holidays
hutch
meals
silverware
table
tablecloth

### Living Room

bookcase
books
company
couch
fireplace
lamp
relax
sofa
statues
table
television
VCR
visit

### Bedroom

| | |
|---|---|
| bed | dresser |
| bedspread | lamp |
| blanket | mirror |
| bookcase | pillow |
| books | sheets |
| bureau | shelf |
| clothes | toys |
| desk | |

### Bathroom

| | |
|---|---|
| bathtub | shampoo |
| cold water | shower |
| comb | sink |
| drain | soap |
| faucet | toilet |
| hair dryer | toothbrush |
| hairbrush | toothpaste |
| hot water | towels |
| medicine | wash cloth |
| rug | |

### Other Things Inside the House

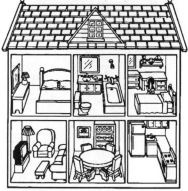

| | |
|---|---|
| attic | floor |
| basement | hallway |
| blinds | laundry |
| ceiling | light switch |
| closet | shades |
| curtains | stairs |
| doorbell | vacuum cleaner |
| drapes | wall |
| electrical outlet | windows |

# Places in Town

What are some places in town where you go to have fun?

Talk about some places in town where people go to do their jobs.

Talk about the stores where your mom and dad buy the things your family eats.

Talk about stores where you go to buy your favorite things.

*A Language Preprimer*

# Places in Town

## Hospital
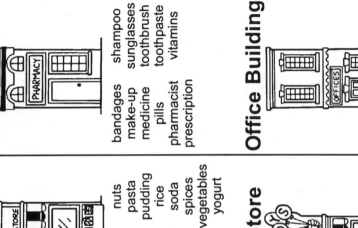

bandages
bed
cast
doctor
medicine
nurse
operation

pills
recovery
thermometer
tray
visit
x-ray

## Library

author
book return
books
card
catalogue
check out
computer
encyclopedia

librarian
library card
magazines
newspapers
subject
tables
title

## Drug Store

bandages
make-up
medicine
pills
pharmacist
prescription

shampoo
sunglasses
toothbrush
toothpaste
vitamins

## Office Building

elevator
entrance
exit
floor
hall

lobby
office
rest room
stairway

## Food Store
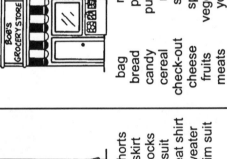

bag
bread
candy
cereal
check-out
cheese
fruits
meats
milk

nuts
pasta
pudding
rice
soda
spices
vegetables
yogurt

## Toy Store

ball
doll
doll house
game
models
play house
puppet
puzzle

race track
stuffed animals
toy car
toy train
video games
yo-yo

## Clothing Store

belt
blouse
dress
gloves
gym suit
hat
pants
shirt

shorts
skirt
socks
suit
sweat shirt
sweater
swim suit

## Flower Shop

bouquet
corsage
flowers
plant
vase

## Bakery

bagel
bread
brownies
cake
cookies

donuts
pastry
pie
rolls

## Fire Station
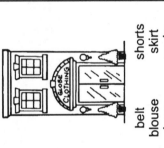

911
ax
boots
coat
dispatch
emergency
fire engine
fire

extinguisher
fire fighter
gloves
helmet
hose
ladder
siren

## Pet Store
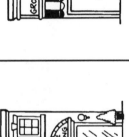

canary
collar
dog biscuit
gerbil
gold fish
hamster
kitten
kitty litter

leash
parakeet
parrot
pet food
pets
puppy

## Pizza Shop
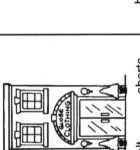

anchovies
cheese
deliver
menu
mushrooms
onions
order

pepperoni
peppers
pizza
restaurant
sausage
slice
waiter

## Words to Help You Talk About Places in Town

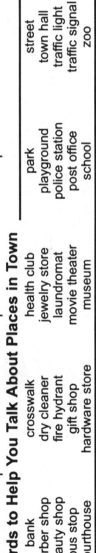

bank
barber shop
beauty shop
bus stop
courthouse

crosswalk
dry cleaner
fire hydrant
gift shop
hardware store

health club
jewelry store
laundromat
movie theater
museum

park
playground
police station
post office
school

street
town hall
traffic light
traffic signal
zoo

# Workers, People Who Make Our Community Better

## Workers, People Who Make our Communities Better

| | | | |
|---|---|---|---|
| actor | coach | librarian | principal |
| artist | cook | lifeguard | sailor |
| astronaut | doctor | mail carrier | soldier |
| baker | electrician | mechanic | teacher |
| banker | farmer | newspaper worker | trash collector |
| barber | fire fighter | nurse | veterinarian |
| builder | fisherman | pilot | waiter |
| bus driver | jeweler | plumber | |
| carpenter | judge | police officer | |

# Workers, People Who Make Our Community Better

Talk about some people who work to help keep the people in your town safe.

Which people will help you when you're sick?

Who will help you to build a house?

Who helps you and your family get the food you need?

Which people build or design or work with things to make things around you more beautiful?

Talk about people who help others to learn.

# Things to Eat

apple
apricot
banana
blueberries
cherries
grapefruit
grapes
orange
peach
pear
pineapple
plum
raisins
strawberries
watermelon

BUTTER

butter
cheese
ice cream
milk
yogurt

MILK

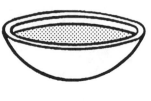

bread
chicken
eggs
hamburger
hot dog
pizza
pork chops
sandwich
soup
steak
tacos

Grape
JELLY

SQUEEZE
MUSTARD

CREAMY
PEANUT
BUTTER

# Things to Eat

beans
broccoli
carrots
celery
cucumbers
lettuce
mushrooms
onions
peas
peppers
radishes
squash
tomatoes

POTATO CHIPS
SNACK-SIZE
6 oz.

candy
cookies
corn chips
cupcakes
nuts
popcorn
potato chips
pretzels

POPCORN

What are some of your favorite things to eat?

What do you like to eat for breakfast? for lunch? for dinner?

What are some things that your family eats or drinks at special family dinners, holidays or parties?

What are some of your favorite things to eat on picnics?

What are your favorite snacks?

Do you ever help cook or bake?

# Things to Wear

# Things to Wear

What are your favorite things to wear?

Talk about some things you wear when you get dressed up for a party or a holiday.

What are some things you wear to keep warm?

What are some things that you wear when it's very warm outside and you want to stay cool?

Talk about some things that you wear to school.

# Things We Use

**Things We Use**

| | | | |
|---|---|---|---|
| backpack | fork | plate | spoon |
| book | glue | rake | string |
| broom, dustpan | hammer | saw | suitcase |
| brush | knife | scissors | tape |
| chalk | nails | shampoo | toothbrush |
| comb | pan | shovel | toothpaste |
| crayon | paper | soap | towel |
| cup | pencil | sponge | umbrella |

*A Language Preprimer*

# Things We Use

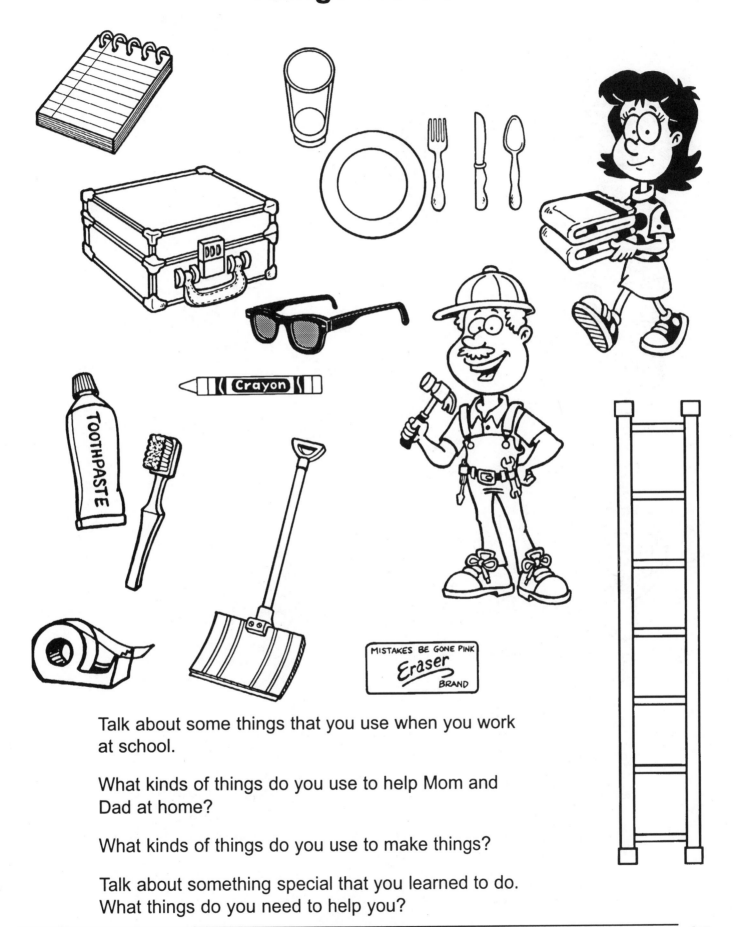

Talk about some things that you use when you work at school.

What kinds of things do you use to help Mom and Dad at home?

What kinds of things do you use to make things?

Talk about something special that you learned to do. What things do you need to help you?

# Favorite Things

**Favorite Things**

| | | |
|---|---|---|
| ball | doll house | puzzle |
| bike | dolls | sled |
| blocks | movies | stuffed animals |
| books | music | toy cars |
| building toys | paints | toy trains |
| clay | party games | toy trucks |
| computer | puppets | yo-yo |

*A Language Preprimer*

# Favorite Things

What are some of your favorite things?

What are some things you like to play with when you're outside?

What are some of your favorite things to do inside your house?

What are some of your favorite things at school?

# Animals

**Animals**

| | | | |
|---|---|---|---|
| alligator | deer | hippopotamus | sea gull |
| ant | dog | horse | shark |
| bear | dolphin | jellyfish | sheep |
| beaver | duck | kangaroo | skunk |
| bumblebee | eagle | lion | snake |
| camel | elephant | monkey | spider |
| cat | fly | parakeet | tiger |
| chicken | fox | rabbit | turkey |
| cow | giraffe | rhinoceros | turtle |
| cricket | goat | robin | zebra |
| crocodile | goldfish | rooster | |

*A Language Preprimer*

# Animals

Do you have a pet?  Do any of your friends have pets?  Talk about what is special about pets.

If you were an animal which animal would you be?  Why?

Have you learned about animals from watching programs on television?  What are some special things about animals that you know?

Animals help us in many ways.  Cows give us milk, chickens give us eggs.  Before there were cars people used to ride horses.  Can you think of other ways in which animals help us?

Some animals like dinosaurs lived a long time ago but don't live here any longer.  Why do you thing that is?

Talk about some animals that you know of that live on a farm, in a jungle, forest or wide open space.

Talk about some animals that live in the water such as fish.

Some animals can fly.  Most of them are birds or insects.  What kinds of birds have you seen or do you know about?

# Things to Ride

**Things to Ride**

| | | | |
|---|---|---|---|
| ambulance | jet plane | rocket ship | tractor |
| bicycle | motorcycle | sailboat | train |
| bus | moving van | ship | tricycle |
| dump truck | pick-up truck | station wagon | tugboat |
| fire engine | police car | subway | wagon |
| helicopter | racing car | taxi cab | van |

*A Language Preprimer*

# Things to Ride

Talk about the vehicle that you ride in most of the time.

Do you know how to ride a bicycle?

Did you ever have to ride for a long, long time to get to a special place? Talk about some things that you do while you're riding in the car for a long time.

Talk about some vehicles that might be needed in an emergency.

Did you ever ride on a train or in an airplane?

Talk about some of your toy or model cars, trucks, trains or airplanes.

# In, Out

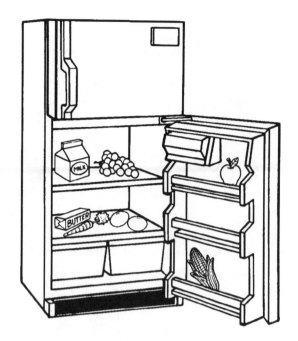

The food is **in** the refrigerator.

The food is **out** of the refrigerator.

The little girl and her father are **out** of the car.

The little girl and her father are **in** the car.

The teddy bear is **in** the box.

The teddy bear is **out** of the box.

What are some things in the room that we're in?

What are some things you put in your backpack? What do you do with these things when you take them out of your backpack?

# Off, On

This man has a hat **on** his head.

Now the hat is **off** the man's head.

The things were **on** the desk.

The wind blew the things **off** the desk.

What are some things on a shelf in the room?

Name some things that are on the table.

Who is sitting on a chair?

Can you see a desk? What is on the desk? Think of some things that should be on a desk.

Name some things on your kitchen counter at home.

Talk about some things on your dresser.

# On, Under

The apple, the pear, the banana and the grapes are **on** the table.

The dog is **under** the table.

The mouse is **on** the chair.

The cat is **under** the chair.

Think about where your hands and feet are when you're sitting at the table. Your hands are on the table. Your feet are under the table.

What do you do when the ball that you're playing with rolls under a car?

This place at the table is set for dinner. The plate, cup, spoon, knife and napkin are **on** the place mat. The napkin is **under** the fork.

Think about this when you help set the table for dinner!

*A Language Preprimer*   ©Circuit Publications

# Over, Under

The boy is going **over** the river.

The bridge is **over** the river.

The swimmer is **under** the bridge.

Look up. What do you see over your head? Look down. What do you see under your feet?

Why do you hold an umbrella over your head when it rains?

You pull a sweat shirt over your head when you put it on. What other clothes do you put on and take off by pulling them over your head?

# Into

The ice cream is going **into** the cone.

The boy is putting clothes **into** the washing machine.

The bus is going **into** the tunnel.

Does your teacher watch the children go back into the room after recess?

When you eat at a restaurant does a waiter pour water into your glass or coffee into Mom's cup?

Someone is pouring too much sugar **into** the bowl.

# In Front, Next to, Behind

The car is **behind** the house.

The cat is **next to** the house.

The dog is **in front** of the house.

The boy is **next to** the chair.

The man is **behind** the chair.

The cupcake is **next to** the bottle.

The carrot is **behind** the bottle.

The apple is **in front of** the bottle.

The girl is **in front of** the chair.

Stand in front of your chair, behind your chair and next to your chair.  Talk about where you are.

Stand in front of a friend, behind a friend and next to a friend.  Talk about where you are.

# Around

The beads are **around** the can.

The cat has a collar **around** her neck.

The children are standing **around** the tree.

Sometimes we sit in a circle. We sit around someone or something special in the middle of the circle.

Do you see anyone wearing something around his or her neck?

Does your family sit around the table when you have dinner?

Do you and your friends sit around the table when you work at school?

# Through

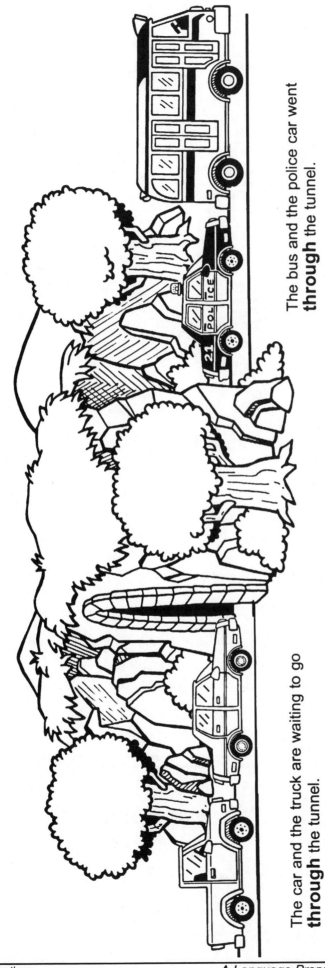

Someone is putting a string through the **bead**.

The bus and the police car went **through** the tunnel.

The car and the truck are waiting to go **through** the tunnel.

Have you ridden in a car or a train that went through a tunnel?

Each time you come into a room you walk through a doorway.

Sometimes you must walk through a hallway to get from one room to another room.

Do you walk through a yard or a parking lot to get to a building?

Sometimes we walk through a store to get from a shopping mall to the parking lot.

# At

These children are **at** school.

Gail is **at** the lumber yard.

This woman is **at** a gas station.

| Hamburgers | | Lemonade | | Ice Cream Cones | |
| --- | --- | --- | --- | --- | --- |
| Small | 🍔 | Small |  | Small |  |
| Medium |  | Medium |  | Medium |  |
| Large |  | Large |  | Large |  |

This boy is **at** the snack bar.

What do you like to do when you're at school?

What do you like to do at the beach?

Have you ever listened to someone read a story at the library?

*A Language Preprimer*

# Here, There, Across

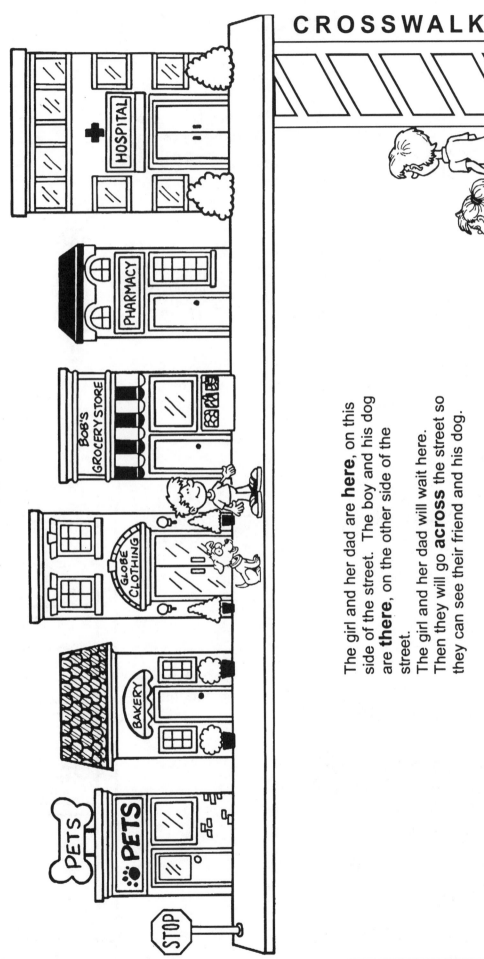

CROSSWALK

HOSPITAL

PHARMACY

BOB'S GROCERY STORE

GLOBE CLOTHING

BAKERY

PETS

STOP

The girl and her dad are **here**, on this side of the street. The boy and his dog are **there**, on the other side of the street.
The girl and her dad will wait here. Then they will go **across** the street so they can see their friend and his dog.

When something is close to you, you say, "It's here." When something is far from you, you say, "It's there."

If you talk to a friend who is across the table from you, you can say, "Here is my paper. There is your paper. Here is my book. There is your book." Your friend would say the same thing talking about her things and your things!

# Between

The boy is standing **between** two girls.

The sheep is **between** the lion and the elephant.

The elephant is **between** the sheep and the tiger.

The tiger is **between** the elephant and the horse.

The police car is **between** the bus and the truck.

The owl is **between** the frog and the bird.

The flower shop is **between** the fire station and the toy store.

# Up, Down

This squirrel is going **up** the tree.

This squirrel is coming **down** the tree.

Did you ever ride an elevator up and down?

Have you ever ridden on an escalator?

How does a kite go up and down?

When you go on the slide at the park which part do you go up? Which part do you go down?

# Above, Below

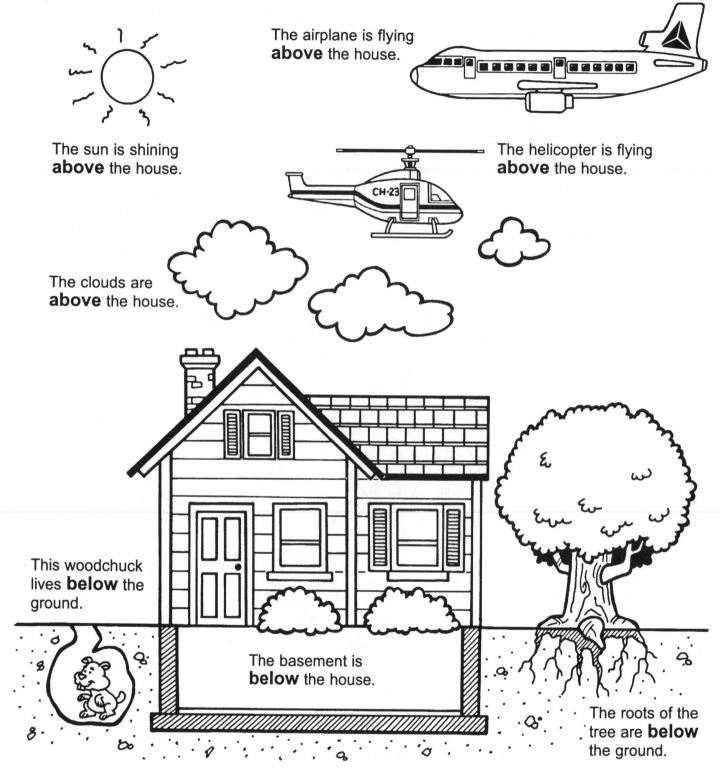

The sun is shining **above** the house.

The airplane is flying **above** the house.

The helicopter is flying **above** the house.

The clouds are **above** the house.

This woodchuck lives **below** the ground.

The basement is **below** the house.

The roots of the tree are **below** the ground.

Can you think of some animals that live below the ground?

What do you see above your head when it's going to rain?

When you stand in your kitchen or living room at home what room or part of the house is above your head? What room or part of the house is below your head?

What parts of your body are above your waist? What parts are below your waist?

*A Language Preprimer* ©Circuit Publications

# First, Last

These cars are waiting to go through the car wash.

This car is **last**.

This car is **first** in line.

Claudia sits in the **first** seat in the row.

Peg sits in the **last** seat.

When the children in your class form a line someone is first and someone is last. Were you ever the first in line? Were you ever the last?

What is the last room down the hall in your school or in your house?

What does the first house on your street look like? What does the last house on your street look like?

# Top, Bottom

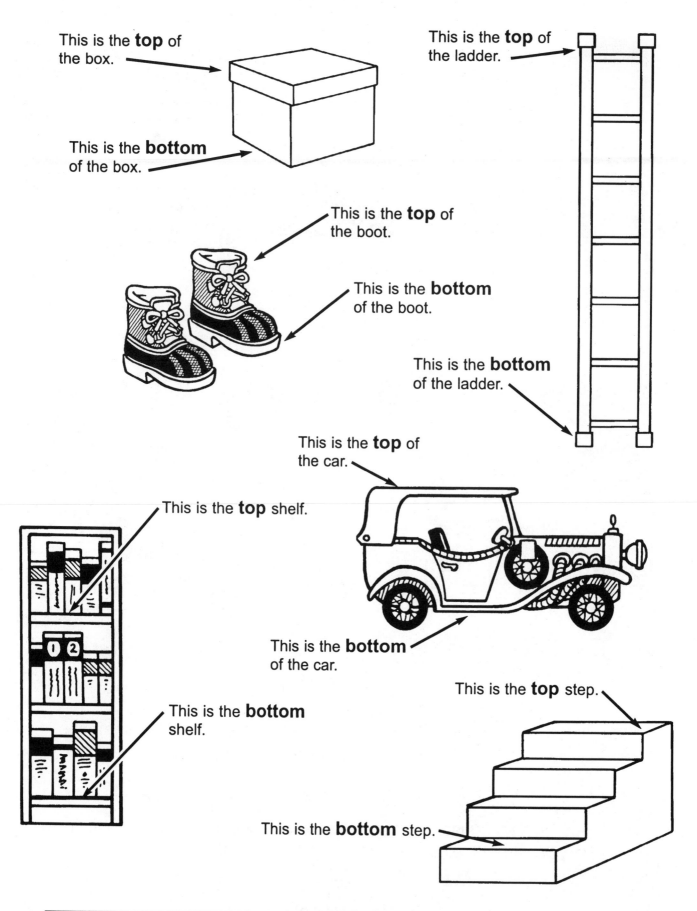

This is the **top** of the box.

This is the **bottom** of the box.

This is the **top** of the ladder.

This is the **top** of the boot.

This is the **bottom** of the boot.

This is the **bottom** of the ladder.

This is the **top** of the car.

This is the **top** shelf.

This is the **bottom** of the car.

This is the **bottom** shelf.

This is the **top** step.

This is the **bottom** step.

# Front, Back

Here are the **fronts** of these animals.

Here are their **backs**.

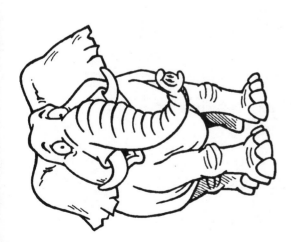
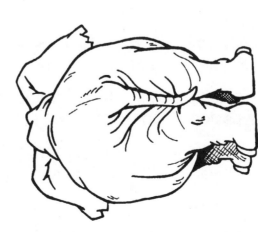

Talk about how each of these animals looks from the front.

Talk about how each one looks from the back.

What do you see when you look at the front of a car?  What do you see when you look at the back of a car?

*A Language Preprimer*    **39**

# Front, Back, Side

This is the **front** of the zebra.     This is the **side** of the zebra.     This is the **back** of the zebra.

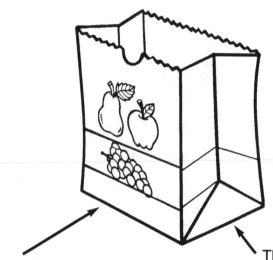 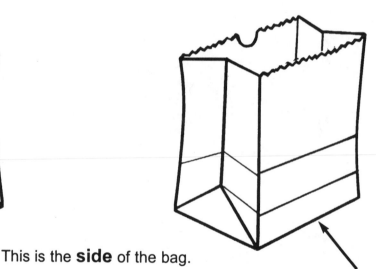

This is the **front** of the bag.

This is the **side** of the bag.

This is the **back** of the bag.

Talk about what you see when you look at the front of your house, the side of your house and the back of your house.

What are some things you see when you look at the front of a car, the back of a car and the side of a car?

What does the front of your school building look like? What does the back and the side of your school building look like?

# Beginning, Middle, End

These children are in line.

Krissy is at the **beginning** of the line.

Roy is in the **middle**.

Bob is at the **end** of the line.

The engine is at the **beginning** of the train.

This is the **middle** car of the train.

The caboose is at the **end** of the train.

This fish is at the **beginning** of this row.

This fish is in the **middle**.

This fish is at the **end** of the row.

Get in line with your friends. Think about who is at the beginning, in the middle and at the end of the line. Then tell everyone to turn around. You'll see that the friend who had been at the **beginning** of the line is now at the **end** of the line!

*A Language Preprimer*

# Right, Left

Claudia is writing with her **right** hand.
Ted is raising his **left** hand.

The man is holding his hat in his **right** hand.

The artist is holding the brush in his **right** hand. He's holding the paints in his **left** hand.

The girl is holding a banana and an apple in her **right** hand.

The girl is holding a plate and a cup in her **left** hand.

This is the elephant's back **left** leg.

This is the elephant's back **right** leg.

Write your name. Start at the **left** side of the paper.

*A Language Preprimer* ©Circuit Publications

# Before, After

Look at this girl's hands **before** she washed them.

This is how her hands looked **after** she washed them.

This is how the man looked **before** he shaved.

This is how he looked **after** he shaved.

This is how the pencil looked **before** the girl sharpened it.

This is how the pencil looked **after** she sharpened it.

What do you do before dinner?

What do you do before you go to the library?

What do you do after you're finished playing with a toy?

# Morning, Afternoon, Evening

The sun rises very early in the **morning**.
**Afternoon** begins in the middle of the day.

**Evening** comes at the end of the day, at the beginning of the night. It's the time when it's just starting to get dark because the sun has set. It's very dark at night when most people are asleep.

Talk about some things that you do in the morning, afternoon and evening.

*A Language Preprimer*

# Day, Night

It's **daytime** now. Shelby looks out the window and sees a bright, sunny sky. She is wearing shorts and a T-shirt and is ready to go outside to play.

It's **night** time now. Shelby looks out the window and sees the dark sky. She is wearing her nightgown and is ready to go to bed.

What happens at your house during the day? How is this different from what happens during the night?

How are things in your town different during the day and at night?

In the daytime birds fly around looking for something to eat. At night most birds are asleep. One bird, the owl, comes out at night and sleeps during the day. What do animals around your house do differently during the day and night?

*A Language Preprimer*

# Now, Later

Jonathan is eating ice cream **now**.

**Later** he will wash his bowl and spoon.

**Now** Dad is driving home from work.

**Later** he will play catch with his son, Nate.

What are you doing now? Talk about some things that you will do later.

What do you think your mom is doing now? What will she probably do later?

What are the children in your class doing now? What do you think they will do later?

# Yesterday, Today, Tomorrow

**Yesterday** Joey bought a present for his friend.

**Today** he is wrapping the present.

**Tomorrow** Joey will give the present to his friend.

What did you and your friends do at school yesterday?  What are you doing at school today?  What will you do at school tomorrow?

What did you eat for lunch, dinner or snack yesterday?  What do you have for lunch or snack today?  What will you have for your snack tomorrow?

What did you wear to school yesterday?  What are you wearing today?  What do you think you might wear tomorrow?

# Until

She won't be able to go fishing **until** summer when it's warm.

She won't be able to go sledding **until** winter when it's cold and there's snow on the ground.

Now it's winter. Ellie is dressed in warm clothes. She will help Mom and Dad shovel snow.

This is Ellie. She's going to play outside with her friends. It's a nice warm day.

How long must you wait until your next birthday?

Do you have any favorite things put away until a later time?

What are some things you can't do until you get home from school?

# First, Last

The **last** thing she did was to paint the dog's name on the front of the dog house.

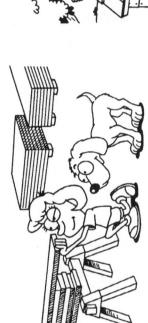

The **first** thing she did was to buy the wood and other things she needed.

Gail wanted to build a dog house for her dog.

The **last** thing he did was to fold the clothes and put them away.

The **first** thing he did was to separate the dark-colored clothes from the light-colored ones.

Joe needed to wash his clothes.

What's the first thing you do when you get to school each day?

What's the last thing you do before you go home from school?

# Always, Never

Our bodies **always** need good food.

We **always** look carefully before we cross the street.

A snowman **never** goes to the beach to get a suntan.

A dog **never** drives a car!

A bird **never** uses rollerblades.

*A Language Preprimer*

# Numbers

Numbers help us tell "how many."  We write numbers using symbols or names of numbers.

one boy

**1**

one

six teddy bears

**6**

six

two girls

**2**
two

seven pears

**7**
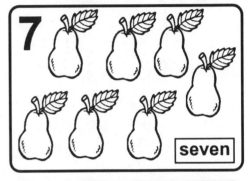
seven

three helicopters

**3**

three

eight cupcakes

**8**

eight

four lions

**4**
four

nine apples

**9**

nine

five police cars

**5**
five

ten mittens

**10**

ten

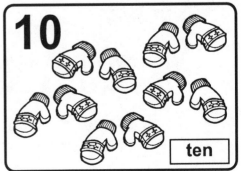

*A Language Preprimer*

# Each

**Each** child has an umbrella.

**Each** dog has a bone.

**Each** vase has two flowers in it.

What is something that each person in your family has?

What is something that each child in your class has?

Talk about something at home or at school that must be shared by everyone, something that each person does not have.

*A Language Preprimer*

# Both

**Both** boys have balloons.

**Both** girls have baseballs.

**Both** of these men have umbrellas. **Both** men have briefcases. Just one of them has a cap.

Look at your feet. Do you have shoes on both feet? Do you have socks on both feet?

Look at your hands. Are both hands clean?

Close both of your eyes. Open both eyes. Now close one eye and open one eye!

# Another

Here is one apple.

Here is **another** apple.

Here is one fish.

Here is **another** fish.

Here is one child.

Here is **another** child.

Here is one squirrel.

Here is **another** squirrel.

Here is one bird.

Here is **another** bird.

Point to one of your fingers.  Point to another finger.  Point to another finger.

Point to something in the room.  Find another one.

When you finish eating something good and you're still hungry do you ask for another one?  What do you enjoy so much that you ask for another one, pizza? cookie? apple? cupcake?

# A, An

Here is **a** banana.

Here is **an** apple.

Here is **a** hot dog.

Here is **an** egg.

Here is **a** cupcake.

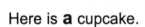

Here is **an** ice cream cone.

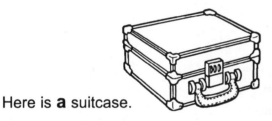

Here is **a** suitcase.

Here is **an** umbrella.

Here is **a** tiger.

Here is **an** elephant.

Which would you rather have, a banana or an apple?

Which one is bigger, a tiger or an elephant?

Which one would help keep you dry, a suitcase or an umbrella?

# Some

some sand

some juice

some soup

some dirt

some milk

some money

some soap

some chalk

some ice cream

some time

Did you drink some milk this morning?

Did you eat some cereal for breakfast?

Do you have some money to spend at the store?

Did you do some work today?

# Few, Many

Here are a **few** grapes.

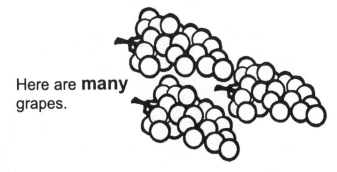

Here are **many** grapes.

Here are **many** children.

Here are a **few** children.

Here are a **few** crayons.

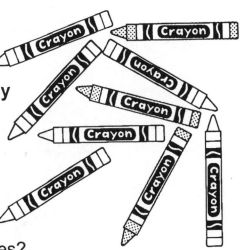

Here are **many** crayons.

Do you have many of some things? Do you have just a few of some things? What kind of things are they?

Do you live on a street with a few houses or many houses?

Are there a few children in this room or many children?

Would you rather have a birthday party with a few friends or many friends?

---

*A Language Preprimer* **57**

# Alone, Together

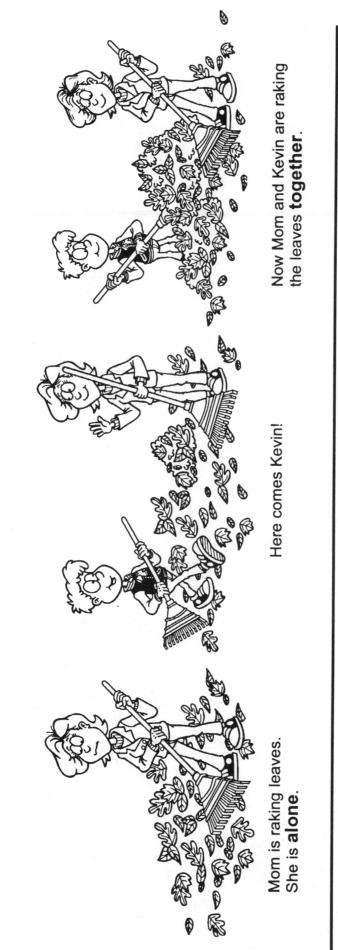

Mom is raking leaves.
She is **alone**.

Here comes Kevin!

Now Mom and Kevin are raking the leaves **together**.

Heidi is fishing.
She is **alone**.

Here comes Megan!

Now Heidi and Megan are fishing **together**.


©Circuit Publications

# Alone, Together

Shannon is swinging. She is **alone**.

Here comes Peggy!

Now Shannon and Peggy are playing on the swings **together**.

Dion is walking. He is **alone**.

Here comes his dog Skipper.

Now Dion and Skipper are walking **together**.

Talk about some things that you like to do when you're alone.

What kinds of things do you enjoy doing together with friends?

# Together, Apart, Separate

During the day Mom and Dad go to work. The children go to school. Everyone goes **separate** ways. The family is **apart**.

In the afternoon or evening everyone is back **together**.

These beads are **together**. They are all on the string.

Now the beads are **separated**.

The cars of this train are **together**.

Now the train is broken **apart**. The cars are **separated**.

Do you have a toy that you can put together or take apart?

Talk about special times when your whole family gets together.

*A Language Preprimer*

# All, Some, None

**All** the popcorn was in the box.

Jane has **some** popcorn.

Mike has **some** popcorn.

But, Ronald has **none**...

...and the popcorn is gone!

There were 4 cupcakes on the tray.

Cassy took **some** cupcakes.

Rodney took **some**.

There were **none** left for Greg.

Are all of the children in your class here today? Are some of the children absent?

If you have some pennies you can keep them all, give some to a friend and some to another friend, then you'll have none left!

When a bottle is full of juice all the juice is in the bottle. If we take some of the juice out of the bottle is all the juice still in the bottle?

When the bottle is empty how much juice is in the bottle?

# Almost

Nancy is **almost** as tall a Mike.

The refrigerator is **almost** empty.

The helicopter is **almost** touching the roof.

The puzzle has **almost** been put together.

The sun is setting. It's **almost** nighttime.

# And

Someone will have a hot dog **and** an apple for lunch.

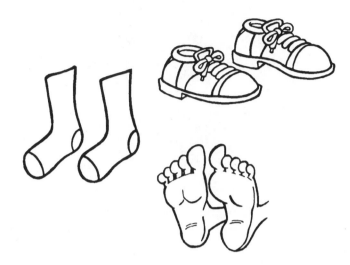

We wear socks **and** shoes on our feet.

Here is a peanut butter **and** jelly sandwich.

The boy **and** his dog are walking.

Do you like peanut butter and jelly sandwiches?

At what time of year do you need mittens and boots?

Talk about things that you and your friends like to do.

# But

This family was planning a picnic. They were happy.

**But** it started to rain and their plans were spoiled.

They were sad.

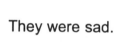

Millie was going to get a cookie.

**But** there were ants all over the box of cookies!

Talk about something you planned for, but didn't happen.

# About

Here is a book **about** dogs.

What is this book **about**?

Here is a book **about** airplanes.

Here is a book **about** cars.

Do you like stories about animals?

Do you like to watch TV shows about children?

What do you and your friends like to talk about?

# Of

This is a picture **of** a house.

This is a picture **of** a giraffe.

This is a picture **of** an airplane.

Here is a box **of** cookies.

Here is a
carton **of** milk.

The girl has a bag
**of** potato chips.

Here is a can
**of** paint.

This suitcase is
full **of** clothes.

The boy has a
box **of** apples.

Do you have a box of crayons?

Do you help Mom or Dad carry bags of groceries into the house?

Do you have pictures of someone or something special in your house?

# Except

All the children have grapes **except** Rodney.

There are apples on every tree **except** the last one.

None of these animals can fly **except** the one in the middle.

Each child is wearing a cap **except** Sue.

# Too (also)

Gumbo has a bone.

Rex has a bone **too**.

Kevin is raking leaves.

Mom is raking leaves **too**.

A car has wheels.

A bus has wheels **too**.

# Too (more than enough)

**Too** much sugar.

**Too** much soup.

**Too** much water.

*A Language Preprimer*

# To (recipient of an action)

The girl is giving a present **to** the boy.

The boy is giving a present **to** the girl.

This boy is giving a bone **to** his dog.

Did you ever give a present to someone?

Did someone give something special to you?

Does your teacher ever ask you to give a note to your mom or dad?

# To (toward)

A boy is going **to** the pizza shop.
A woman is going **to** the flower shop.
A boy is going **to** the toy shop.

A boy is going **to** the pet shop.
A man is going **to** the bakery.
A girl is going **to** the library.

*A Language Preprimer*
©Circuit Publications

# To (purpose)

went to the **to** buy a

went to the **to** buy some

went to the **to** borrow a

went to the **to** buy a

went to the **to** buy some

went to the **to** buy a

went into the burning building **to** rescue the

# Ready

Kevin is **ready** to rake leaves.

Megan is **ready** to go fishing.

Ellie is **ready** to shovel snow.

Mr. Johnson is **ready** to build something.

What do you do to get ready for school?

What do you do to help Mom and Dad get ready for dinner?

What do you do to get ready to play a game that you like?

What do Mom and Dad do to get ready for your favorite holiday?

*A Language Preprimer*  ©Circuit Publications

# Old, Young

This man is **old**.

This baby is **young**.

Grandma is **older** than Mom.

Mom is **older** than Alice.

Alice is **younger** than Mom or Grandma.

How can you tell that someone is old?

Do you have cousins or friends who are older than you?  Do you have any cousins or friends who are younger than you?

Think of some children, grown-ups or special characters in your favorite stories or movies.  Talk about how old you think they are.

# Old, New

These buildings are **old**.

This car is **new**.

This car is **old**.

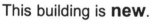

This building is **new**.

This shoe is **new**.

This shoe is **old**.

These jeans are **old**.

These jeans are **new**.

Is your house old or new?

What happens when a car gets old?

Some things are very special and beautiful because they are old. Some people have things in their homes that belonged to their grandparents. Do you have anything in your house that is special because it is very old?

What do you do with your clothes when they are too old to wear?

# Short, Long

This boy is wearing **short** pants.

Now he is wearing **long** pants.

This girl has **long** hair.

Now she has **short** hair.
What do you think happened?

This dog has a **short** tail.

This dog has a **long** tail.

Do you have long or short hair?

Do you know someone who has very long hair?  Do you know someone who has very short hair?

Look at the curtains on the windows in your house or at school.  Are they long, all the way to the floor?  Are they short, just to the bottom of the windows?

Which animals can you think of that have long tails?

# Short, Tall

This man is **tall**.

This child is **short**.

This ladder is **short**.

This ladder is **tall**.

The sheep is not as **tall** as the giraffe.

Who is the tallest in your family?  Who is the shortest?

Who is the tallest child in your class?

Are there any very tall trees on your street?

# Fast, Slow

A tortoise walks **slowly**.

A horse runs **fast**.

The mouse is running **faster** than the cat.

The cat is running **faster** than the dog.

When you are going somewhere and you want to get there fast what do you do?

When you are going somewhere and you want to get there but you don't want to get there very fast what do you do?

Did you ever run in a race? Did you ever swim in a race?

# Hard, Soft

A pillow is **soft**.

A rock is **hard**.

A cap is **soft**.

A helmet is **hard**.

Snow is **soft**.

Ice is **hard**.

Did you ever pet a soft, furry dog or cat?

What are some things to eat that are soft?  What are some things to eat that are hard?

Why do you think a bike helmet is hard?

# Hot, Cold

The stove is **hot**.

The icicles are **cold**.

When it's **hot** outside we wear clothes that will help us keep **cool**.

When it's **cold** outside we wear clothes that will help us keep **warm**.

The sun is too **hot**! The snowman is melting! What would help the snowman stop melting?

Talk about some of the clothes you wear to keep warm.

What do you like to do when it's hot outside?

Talk about some things to eat that are warm.

What are some things to eat that are cold?

# With, Without

Here is a hot dog **without** mustard.

Here is a hot dog **with** mustard.

Here is a slice of toast **without** butter.

Here is a slice of toast **with** butter.

Here is some ice cream **with** chocolate syrup.

Here is a waffle **without** syrup.

Here is some ice cream **without** chocolate syrup.

Here is a waffle **with** syrup.

Look at the zebra. He looks like a horse **with** stripes!

Do you like hot dogs with or without mustard?

Do you like ice cream with or without chocolate syrup?

# Open, Closed

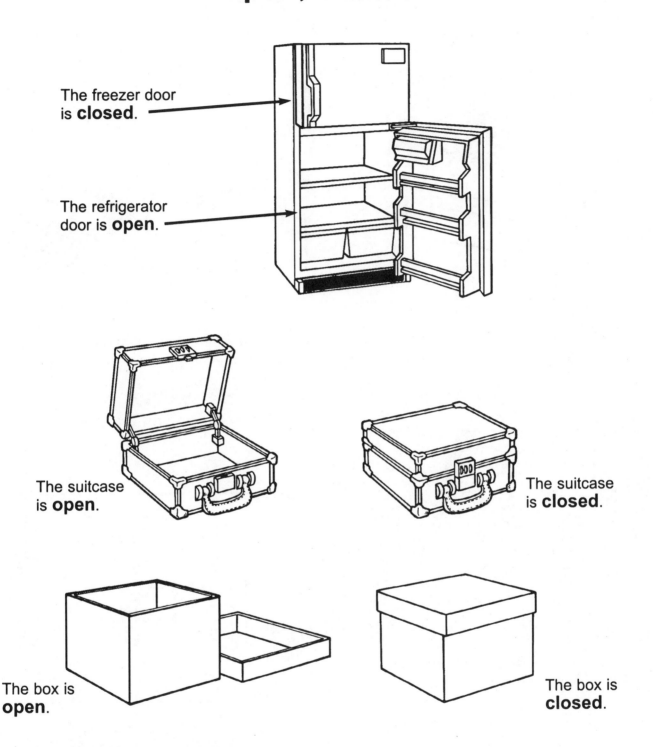

The freezer door is **closed**.

The refrigerator door is **open**.

The suitcase is **open**.

The suitcase is **closed**.

The box is **open**.

The box is **closed**.

On a warm summer day we open the windows. On a cold winter day we close the windows. Why is this?

Why do you open and close doors of buildings, cars, rooms?

You open bottles, jars and boxes when you need to take something out of them. Why is it important to close them when you are finished?

# Dark, Light

The black cat was sitting on the **light**-colored chair.  When the cat got off the chair, some **dark** hairs were on the chair where the cat had been sitting.  Do you know why?

The room is **dark**.  The lights are not turned on.

Now the room is **light**.
What did the man do?

Do you have some light-colored and some dark-colored clothes?

Is the carpet and furniture in your living room light or dark?

During the day the sky is light.  What are some things you can do to make a room a little darker during the day?

*A Language Preprimer*                    ©Circuit Publications

# Full, Empty

This refrigerator is **full**.

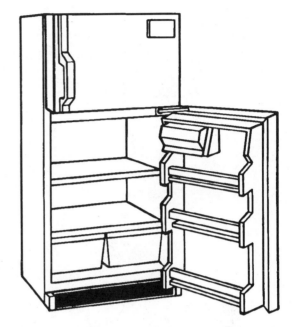

This refrigerator is **empty**.

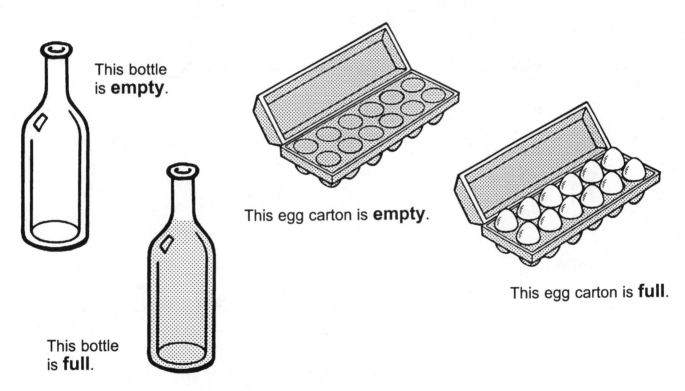

This bottle is **empty**.

This egg carton is **empty**.

This egg carton is **full**.

This bottle is **full**.

What do you do when a bottle or can is empty? Do you throw it away or do you recycle it? Why should we try to recycle empty bottles and cans?

How do you feel when your tummy is empty?

# Wet, Dry

The girl is **wet**.

The girl is **dry**.

The dog is **wet**.

The dog is **dry**.

The girl has **wet** towels.

The girl has some **dry** towels.

What would happen if you didn't dry your hands after you washed them?

What does a dog do to help dry himself off after a bath?

How do Mom and Dad get wet clothes to dry?

What would happen if you sat on a bench that had just been painted and the paint was still wet?

# High, Low

The girl's kite is up **high**.

The boy's kite is down **low**.

There is snow **high** up on the mountain.

What are some things in this room that are too high for you to reach them?

What are some things on the highest shelf in this room or in your classroom?

When does Mom or Dad need to use a ladder?

Can you think of some animals that climb or stay in high places?

Can you think of some animals that like to stay low, near the ground?

# Near, Far, This, That

I am **near this** tree.
**This** cat is **near** me.

I am **far** from **that** tree.
**That** boy and **that** dog
are **far** away from me.

What is the nearest building to your house?

Does your good friend live near you or far away from you?

*A Language Preprimer*

# Wide, Narrow

This picture is **wide**.

This door is **wide**.

This door is **narrow**.

This picture is **narrow**.

This stove is **wide**.

This stove is **narrow**.

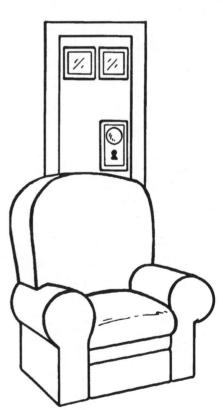

This chair is too **wide** to fit through the doorway!

Are the doors in your house wide or narrow?

Is your garage door wider or narrower than the front door to your house?

Do you have a mirror over your dresser?  Is it wide or narrow?

Look at both things in each of these boxes. Tell if both things are the **same** or **different**. Tell why.

Are these animals the **same** or **different**?

They're the **same**.
They are both elephants.

Are these vegetables the **same** or **different**?

They are **different**. One is a carrot, the other one is corn.

Are these fruits the **same** or **different**?

Are these treats the **same** or **different**?

Are these things that grow the **same** or **different**?

Are these animals the **same** or **different**?

*A Language Preprimer*

Look at both things in each of these boxes. Tell if both things are the **same** or **different**. Tell why.

| | |
|---|---|
| Are these things to write with the **same** or **different**?  | Are these things to wear the **same** or **different**?  |
| Are these things to ride the **same** or **different**?  | Are these animals the **same** or **different**?  |
| Are these chairs the **same** or **different**? | Are these houses the **same** or **different**? 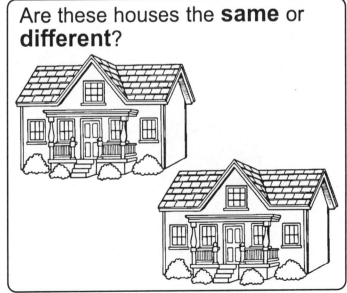 |

*A Language Preprimer*

Talk about **parts** of something or someone.

Here is a house.

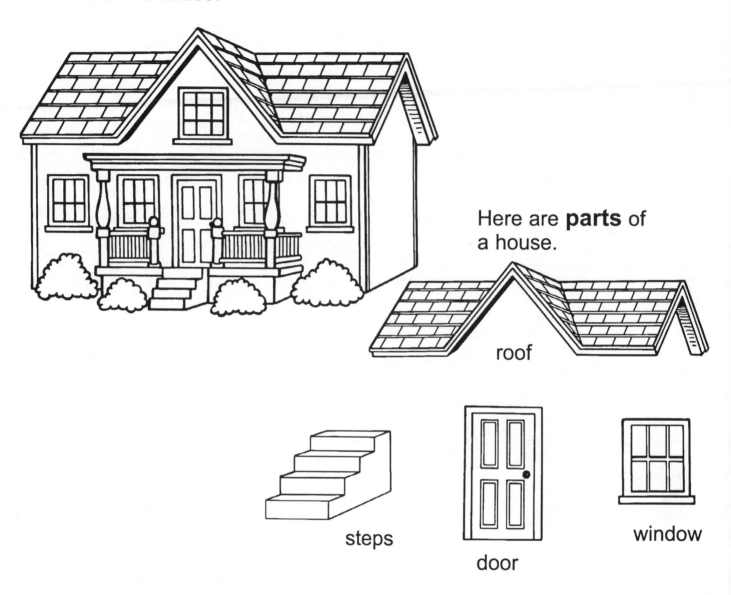

Here are **parts** of
a house.

roof

steps

door

window

Here are **parts** of a person.

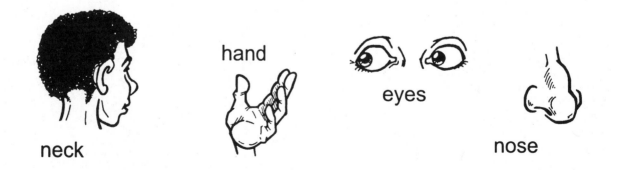

neck

hand

eyes

nose

*A Language Preprimer*

# Talk about **parts** of some thing or animal.

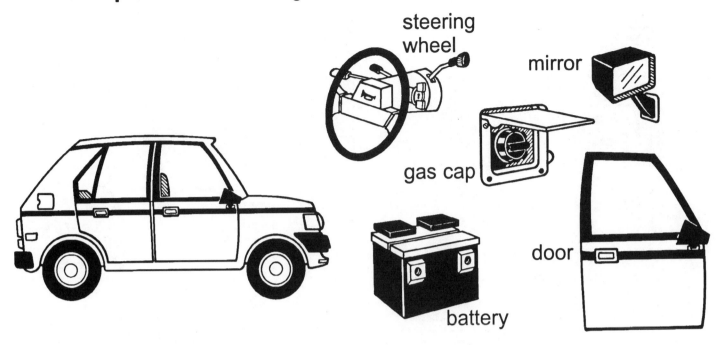

This is a car.           These are **parts** of a car.

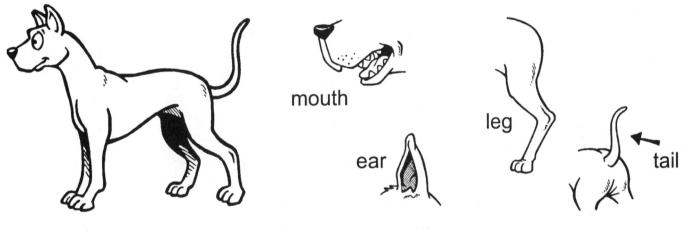

This is a dog.           These are **parts** of a dog.

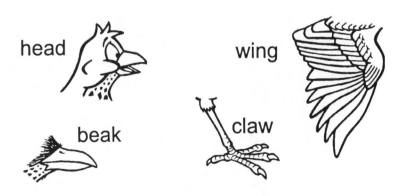

This is a bird.          These are **parts** of a bird.

Talk about why these things **go together**.

Example:

These go together because you need a **paint brush** and **paint** to paint something.

*A Language Preprimer*

# Talk about why these things **go together**.

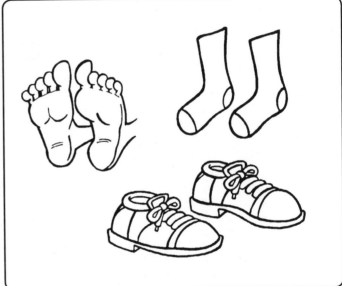

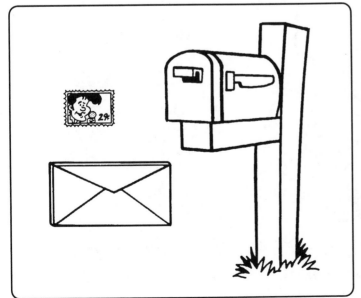

Look at the people or things in each row and **compare** them.

This woman is **young**.　This girl is **younger**.　This baby is the **youngest**.

This tree is **tall**.　This tree is **taller**.　This tree is the **tallest**.

This girl has **some** ice cream.　This girl has **more** ice cream.　This boy has the **most** ice cream.

*A Language Preprimer*

Look at the animals, people or things in each row and **compare** them.

The dog is running **fast**.    The cat is running **faster**.    The mouse is running **fastest**.

This girl's kite is flying **high**.    This girl's kite is flying **higher**.    This girl's kite is flying **highest**.

Here is a **good** treat.    Here is a **better** treat.    Here is the **best** treat.

Follow the directions.

Draw a line to the shapes that **match** each other.

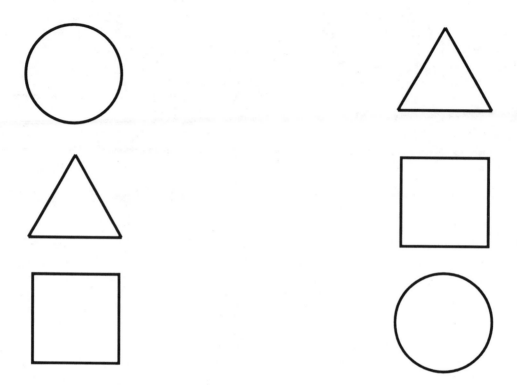

**Connect the dots** and you will draw a special shape.

*A Language Preprimer*

Follow the directions.

Draw a **line under** the animals that can fly.

Draw a **circle around** the animals that live in the water.

**Follow** this path and help this squirrel find the acorns.

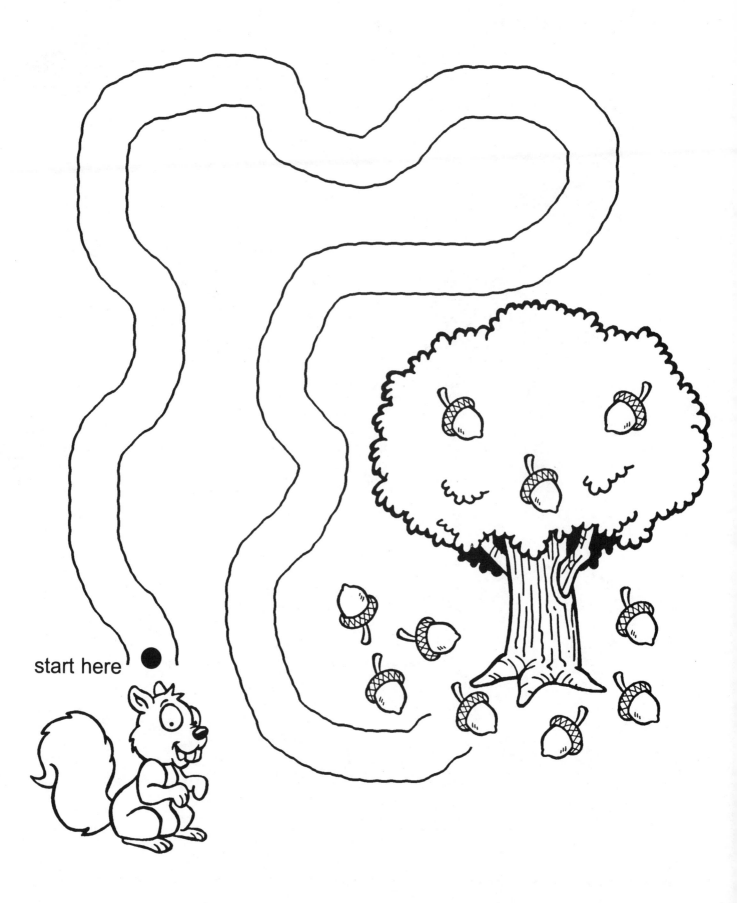

start here

*A Language Preprimer*

©Circuit Publications

Follow the directions.

**Trace** the lines and you will draw a house.

**Copy** these shapes. Draw them on the line below.

 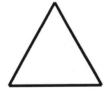 

_____

Draw a line connecting two things that **rhyme**.

An animal that rhymes with hat.

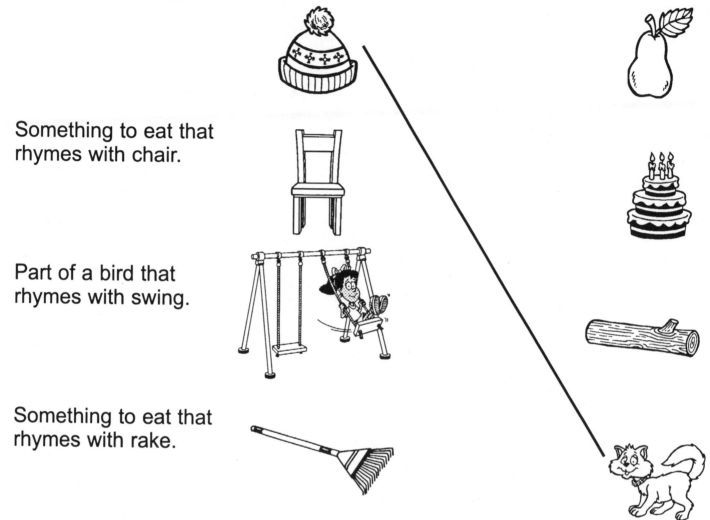

Something to eat that rhymes with chair.

Part of a bird that rhymes with swing.

Something to eat that rhymes with rake.

Part of a face that rhymes with pie.

Part of a tree that rhymes with dog.

*A Language Preprimer*

©Circuit Publications

Draw a line connecting two things that **rhyme**.

Something for drying your
hands that rhymes with owl.

Part of a car that rhymes
with feet.

An animal that rhymes
with dish.

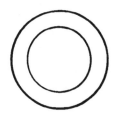

A person that rhymes
with toy.

Part of an animal that
rhymes with egg.

A place to live that
rhymes with mouse.

Think about **opposites**.

**Big** is the **opposite** of **little**.

**Same** is the **opposite** of **different**.

**Whole** is the **opposite** of **part**.

**Off** is the **opposite** of **on**.

**Old** is the **opposite** of **new**.

**Long** is the **opposite** of **short**.

Think about **opposites**.

**Wet** is the **opposite** of **dry**.

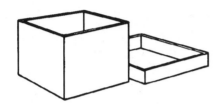 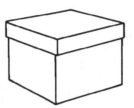

**Open** is the **opposite** of **closed**.

**Front** is the **opposite** of **back**.

**Alone** is the **opposite** of **together**.

**Empty** is the **opposite** of **full**.

**Narrow** is the **opposite** of **wide**.

Things are made from different **materials**.

These things are made from **cloth**.

These things are made from **glass**.

These things are made from **leather**.

*A Language Preprimer*

Things are made from different **materials**.

These things are made from **wood**.

These things are made from **metal**.

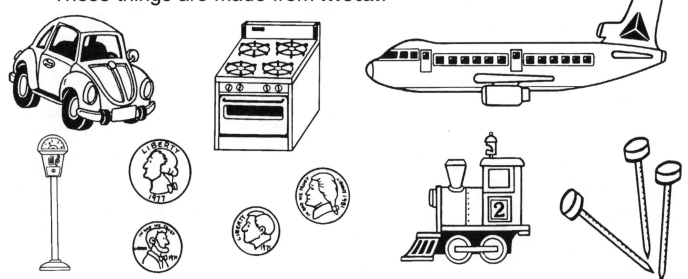

These things are made from **paper** or **cardboard**.

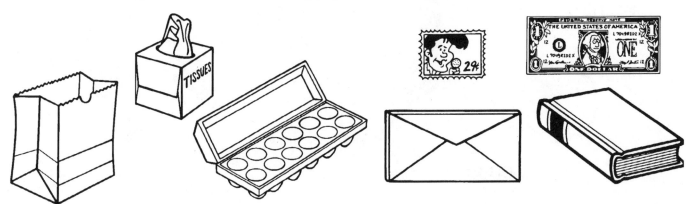

Things come in different kinds of **containers**.

Some things come in **boxes**.

tissues

cake mix

crayons

crackers

rice

cereal

Some things come in **cans**.

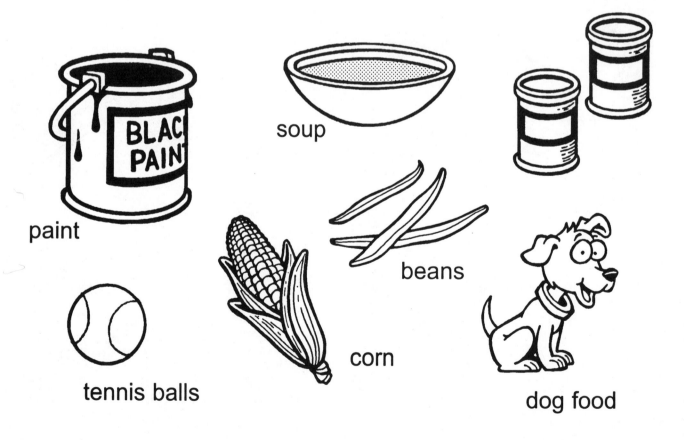

paint

soup

beans

tennis balls

corn

dog food

*A Language Preprimer*

©Circuit Publications

Things come in different kinds of **containers**.

Some things come in **bottles** or **jars**.

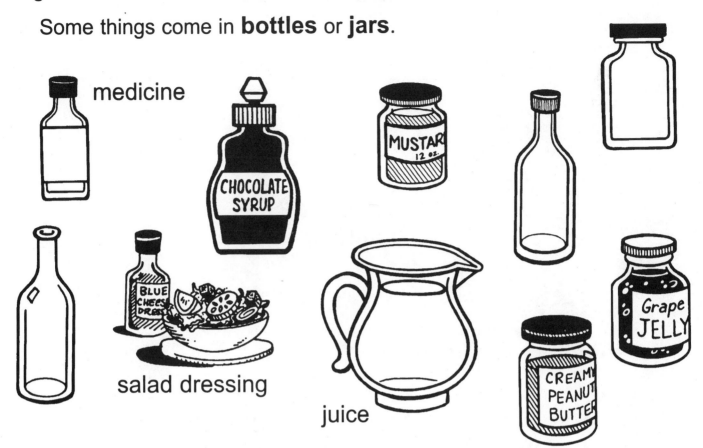

medicine

CHOCOLATE SYRUP

MUSTARD 12 oz.

salad dressing
BLUE CHEESE DRESS

juice

CREAMY PEANUT BUTTER

Grape JELLY

Some things come in **bags**.

POTATO CHIPS SNACK-SIZE 6 OZ.

candy
SALT WATER TAFFY

FLOUR

WHITE BREAD

Some things come in **cartons**.

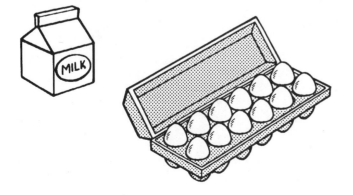

MILK

Toothpaste comes in a **tube**.

# Action Words

work

sleep

point

sing

dance

run

talk

jump

blow

hit

ride

*A Language Preprimer*

# Action Words

run

give

stand

fly

eat

write

climb

drive

walk

swing

pull

carry

drink

catch

throw

# What are these things used for?

 **for** playing

 **for** helping someone see better

 **for** cutting

 **for** reading

 **for** brushing my teeth

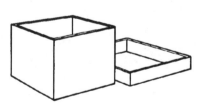 **for** riding

 **for** shoveling snow

 **for** putting things in

**for** keeping things cold

 **for** cooking and baking

# Feelings

sad

happy

angry

timid or shy

confused

scared

# Baby Animals

Animal **babies** sometimes have different names than animal "grown-ups."

A **kitten** is a **baby** cat.

A **tadpole** is a **baby** frog.

A **puppy** is a **baby** dog.

A **lamb** is a **baby** sheep.

*A Language Preprimer* ©Circuit Publications

# Baby Animals

Animal **babies** sometimes have different names than animal "grown-ups."

A **calf** is a **baby** cow.

A **duckling** is a **baby** duck.

A **cub** is a **baby** bear.

A **colt** is a **baby** horse.

# Shapes

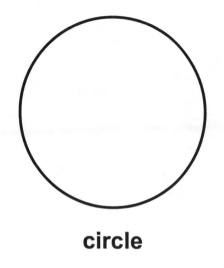

**circle**

**square**

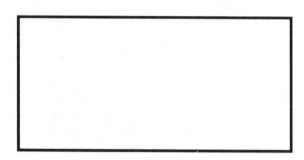

**rectangle**

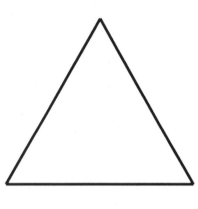

**triangle**

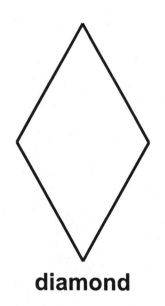

**diamond**

**star**

*A Language Preprimer*

©Circuit Publications

# Weather

**rainy**

**windy**

**cloudy**

**stormy**

**cold**

**sunny**

# Using Pronouns

The following pages present a familiar experience in the lives of many young children, making peanut butter and jelly sandwiches!  This scenario is presented as a sequence of events involving children sharing something that each of them has and ultimately having a snack together.

The purpose of this activity is to offer you as a teacher a chance to guide children to attend to and express a variety of pronouns: *we*, *me*, *us*, *he*, *she*, *they*, *them*, *anyone*, *everyone*.  This simple sequence should be presented as a story.  Then, using the characters and props on pages 120 and 121, it can be used as a simple dramatization where children retell and dramatize the events of the story.

Retelling the events in this familiar scenario will provide many opportunities for children to use third person pronouns (*he*, *she*, *they*, *them*) and indefinite pronouns (*anyone*, *everyone*).  If two or more children dramatize this story and try to role-play the parts of the characters, they will also use first and second person pronouns (*I*, *me*, *we*, *us*, *our*, *you*, *your*).

The character and prop cut-outs on pages 120 and 121 can be colored, cut out and pasted on heavy stock and be used over and over again.

# A Story about Friends

Here is Laurie. She has some jelly.

Here is Ben. He has some peanut butter.

Here are Pete and Tom.
They have some bread.

Pete said to Ben, "Tom and I have bread, but we have no peanut butter. We need some peanut butter for our bread. Will you give us some of your peanut butter?"

Ben said, "Yes, I'll give you some peanut butter for your bread." Then he said, "I need some bread for my peanut butter. Will you give me some bread for my peanut butter?"

Pete and Tom said, "Yes, we will give you some bread."

Ben gave Pete and Tom some peanut butter.

Tom gave Ben some bread.

Laurie said, "I have some jelly.  We can make peanut butter and jelly sandwiches."

She asked, "Ben, can I have some peanut butter?"

Ben said, "Yes."

She asked, "Pete and Tom, can I have some bread?"

Tom said, "Yes."

  Laurie gave Pete, Tom and Ben some jelly.

Everyone made peanut butter and jelly sandwiches.

Just then Judy came in. She said, "Hi everyone! I have some apples. My mom just bought them at the market. Would anyone like an apple?" she asked.

Pete, Tom, Laurie and Ben all said, "Yes, thank you." Judy gave apples to everyone.

Ben asked, "Judy, would you like a peanut butter and jelly sandwich?"

She said, "Yes, thank you."

Ben and Tom made a peanut butter and jelly sandwich for Judy.

Everyone ate their sandwiches and their apples. They all had a nice snack.

Laurie

Ben

Pete

Tom

Judy

*A Language Preprimer*

©Circuit Publications

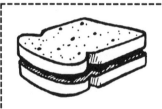